big
NATE
I CAN'T TAKE IT!

More

big NATE

adventures from

LINCOLN PEIRCE

Novels:

Big Nate: In a Class By Himself
Big Nate Strikes Again
Big Nate On a Roll
Big Nate Goes For Broke
Big Nate Flips Out

Activity Books:

Big Nate Boredom Buster
Big Nate Fun Blaster
Big Nate Doodlepalooza

Comic Compilations:

Big Nate From the Top
Big Nate Out Loud
Big Nate and Friends
Big Nate: What Could Possibly Go Wrong?
Big Nate: Here Goes Nothing
Big Nate Makes the Grade
Big Nate All Work and No Play
Big Nate Game On!
Big Nate: Genius Mode

big NATE

I CAN'T TAKE IT!

by LINCOLN PEIRCE

SCHOLASTIC INC.

ISBN 978-0-545-66703-6

12 11 10 9 8 7 6 5 4 3 2 1   14 15 16 17 18 19/0

Printed in the U.S.A.   40

First Scholastic printing, January 2014

30

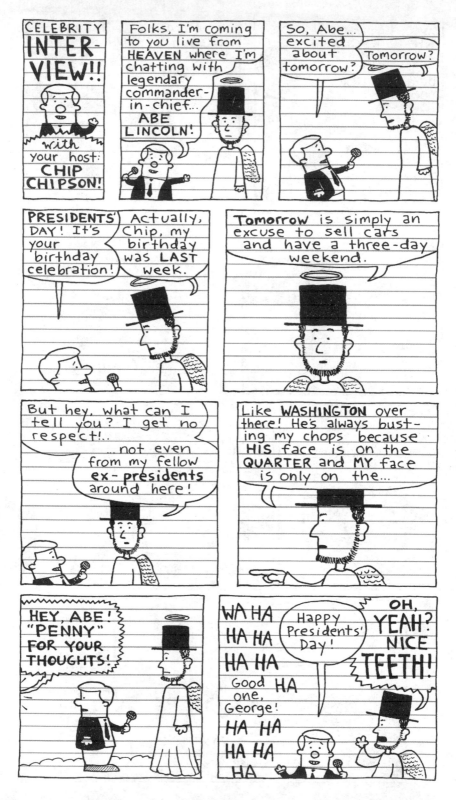

58

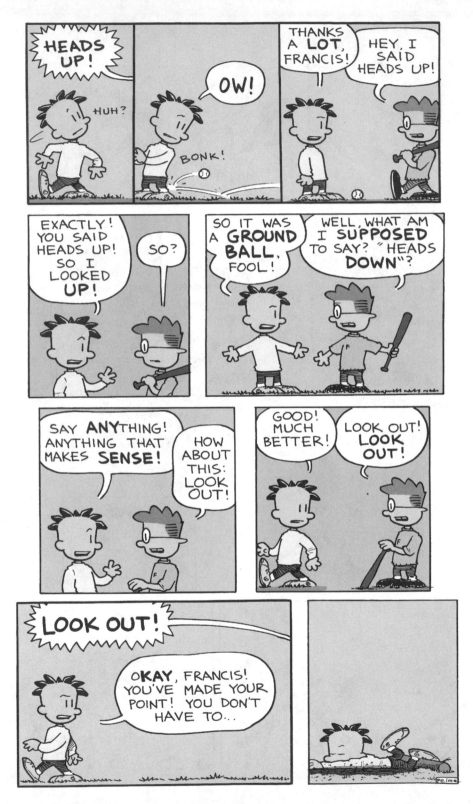

96

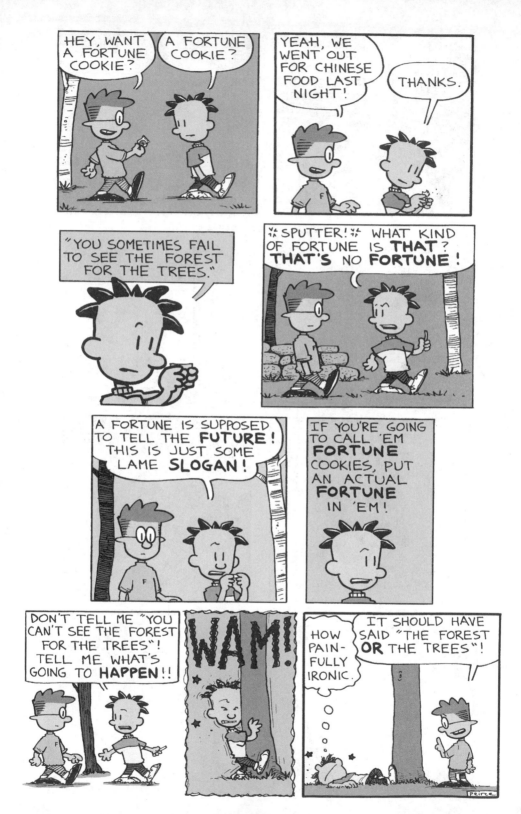

$ "Money Matters" $ $
with your host
BIFF BIFFWELL
and special guest...
CONSUMER REPORTER CELINE PAYCHEK!!
Hi, Celine!
Nice to be here, Biff!
Celine, it's BACK-TO-SCHOOL time again! Any shopping tips for parents trying to save a few pennies?
Absolutely, Biff!
DON'T be fooled by all the so-called "SALES"! That's the stuff the stores WANT you to buy!
Instead, check out the items marked "CLEARANCE"!
Your 11-year-old son might want a backpack like everyone ELSE's, but WHY PAY MORE?
Here's a perfectly good "Pinky the Pony" pack for HALF THE COST!
Pinky
... And Biff, who needs some fancy-pants NOTEBOOK with all those pockets, compartments, and zippers?
This plain brown binder is a STEAL, and the water damage is MINIMAL!
Then, of course, there's the matter of CLOTHES! Your children might beg you for "NICE" clothes that "FIT" and "LOOK GOOD"! ... AND, might I add, cost an ARM and a LEG!
Why pay through the nose? What's more important: some pair of pants your kid's going to outgrow... OR SAVING YOUR PRECIOUS, HARD-EARNED MONEY??
WE'LL TAKE 'EM!
SIGH...
CLE
CLEARAN
Peirce

139

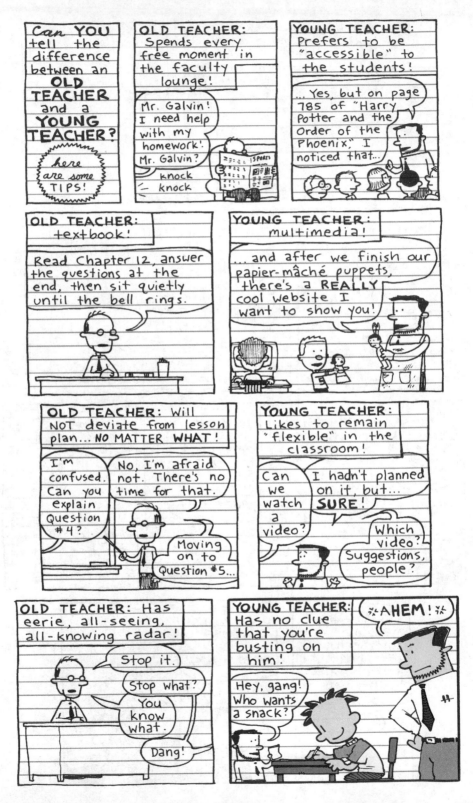

174

179

Welcome once again to... "MILD WORLD of SPORTS"
with BIFF BIFFWELL!
Hello, friends! Today we'll be treated to a gala FIGURE SKATING exhibition! Here to provide commentary is TODD ZAMBONI!
HI Biff!
Todd, who's our first skater?
It's ELLEN WRIGHT, unveiling a new program!
CLAP!
CLAP!
CLAP!
CLAP!
CLAP!
...And here comes her first jump!
She INVENTED that move! It's called the "ugly duckling"!
And now... a combination jump!
Yes, it's a combination of CLUMSINESS and INEPTITUDE!
WOW, Todd! What choreography!
I agree, Biff! WHAT choreography??
Like all good routines, this one tells a story!
Right, Biff! It's the story of an awkward girl who can't skate very well!
I must say, Todd, Ellen has some UNUSUAL moves!
She sure does! There's no telling what she'll do NEXT!
!
THAT'S A MOVE I'VE NEVER SEEN BEFORE
Peirce